Sparkle, sparkle, sparkle...
Princesses love to wear diamond tiaras and necklaces.

Swish, swish, swish...
Princess Kate loves dancing in long, flowing dresses.

Chatter, chatter, chatter...
Princess Jasmine loves talking to her friends on the cell phone.

Zzz, zzz, zzz...

This princess has been asleep for one hundred years!

Tweet, tweet, tweet...
Princess Aurora sings to the birds from high up in a tower.

Brush, brush, brush...

Princesses brush their hair one hundred times before bed.

Stir, whisk, stir...

Princess Amber likes to bake fancy cupcakes for her friends and family.

Hello, hello, hello...

Princess Jemima is very polite and waves to people from her royal carriage.

Shimmer, shimmer, shimmer...
Princess Isis loves to dance beneath
the chandeliers in the royal ballroom.